Easy Jazz & Blues fo.

Jazz Tunes

You've Always Wanted To Play

*arranged
for
piano
by
Stephen
Duro*

CHESTER MUSIC

(A division of Music Sales Ltd.)

8-9 Frith Street, London, W1V 5TZ
Exclusive distributors: Music Sales Ltd., Newmarket Road,
Bury St Edmunds, Suffolk, IP33 3YB

A Night In Tunisia

Words by Raymond Leveen. Music by Frank Paparelli & John 'Dizzy' Gillespie

Angel Eyes

Words by Earl Brent, Music by Matt Dennis

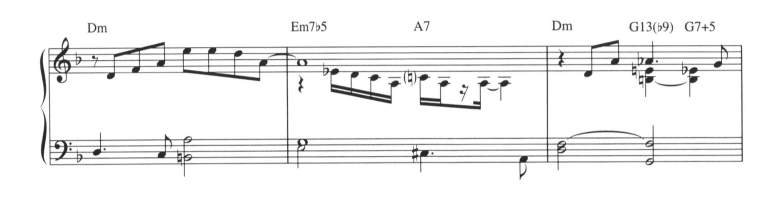

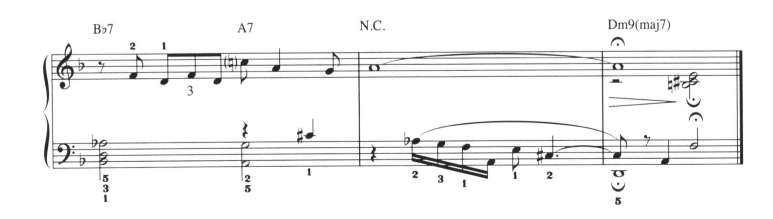

Basin Street Blues

Words & Music by Spencer Williams

Moderate blues tempo

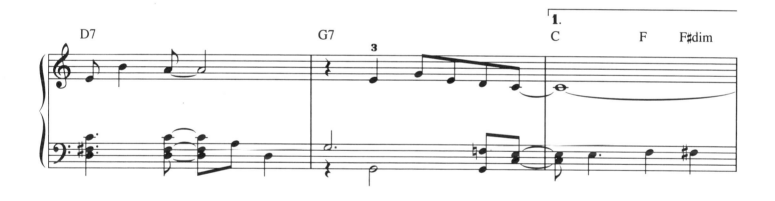

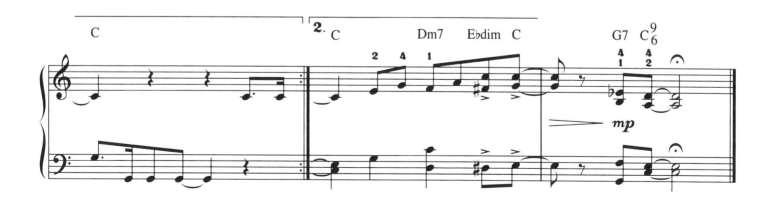

Bernie's Tune

By Bernie Miller

Moderately fast

Between The Devil And The Deep Blue Sea

Words by Ted Koehler. Music by Harold Arlen

19

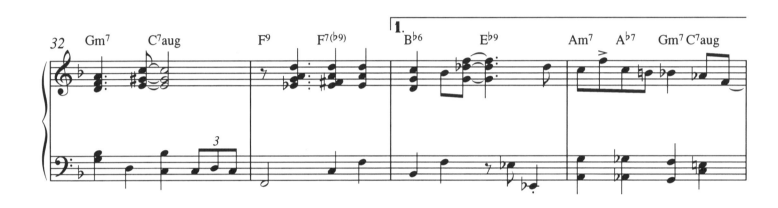

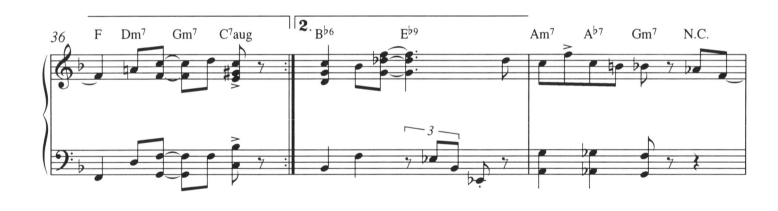

Blue And Sentimental

Words and Music by Count Basie, Jerry Livingston & Mack David

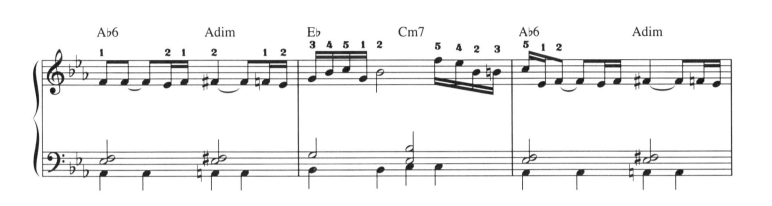

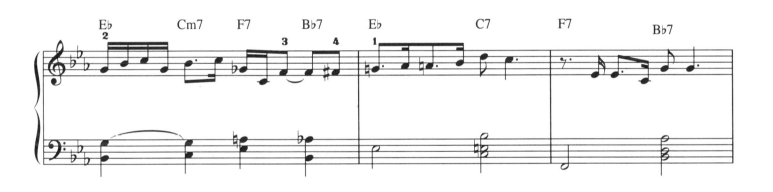

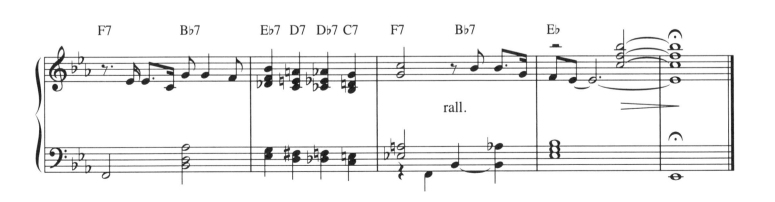

Blues In The Night
(My Mamma Done Tol' Me)

Words by Johnny Mercer. Music by Harold Arlen

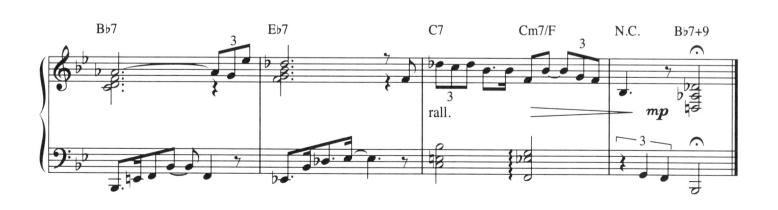

Bluesette

Words by Norman Gimbel. Music by Jean Thielemans

Moderately bright

Chelsea Bridge

By Billy Strayhorn

Come Fly With Me

Lyrics by Sammy Cahn. Music by James Van Heusen

Don't Worry 'Bout Me

Words by Ted Koehler. Music by Rube Bloom.

Fascinating Rhythm

Music & Lyrics by George Gershwin & Ira Gershwin

Fly Me To The Moon (In Other Words)

Words & Music by Bart Howard

Georgia On My Mind

Words by Stuart Gorrell. Music by Hoagy Carmichael.

Moderately slow

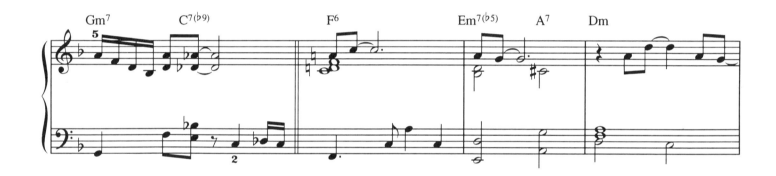

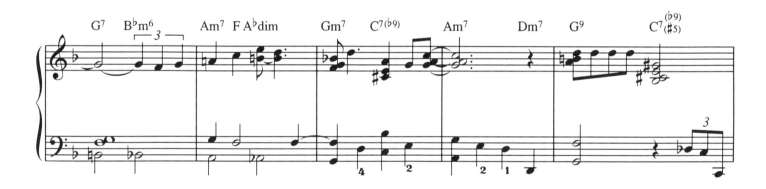

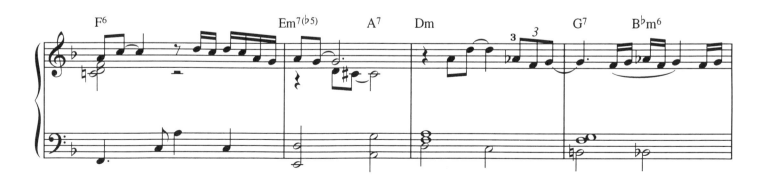

Gone, Gone Gone

Words & Music by George Gershwin, Ira Gershwin, Dubose & Dorothy Heyward

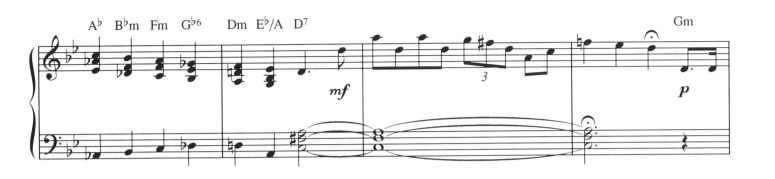

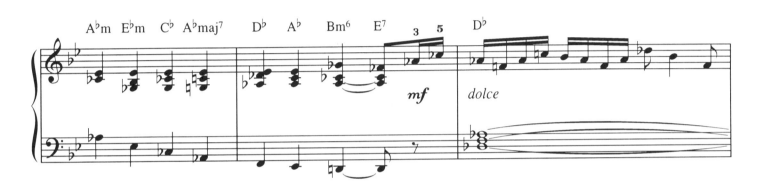

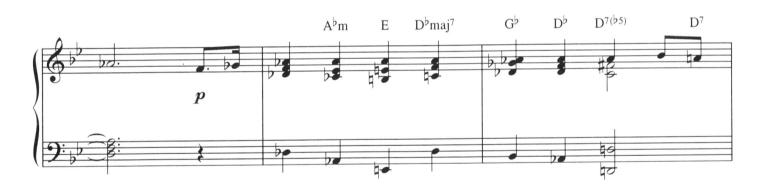

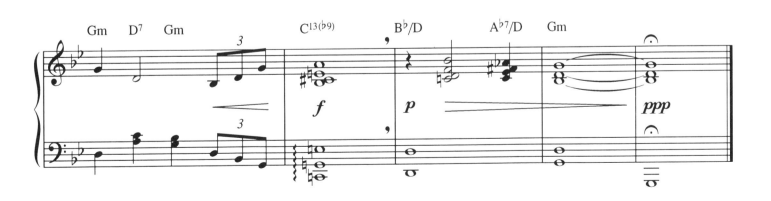

Here's That Rainy Day

Words & Music by Johnny Burke & Jimmy Van Heusen

51

Honeysuckle Rose

Words by Andy Razaf. Music by Thomas 'Fats' Waller

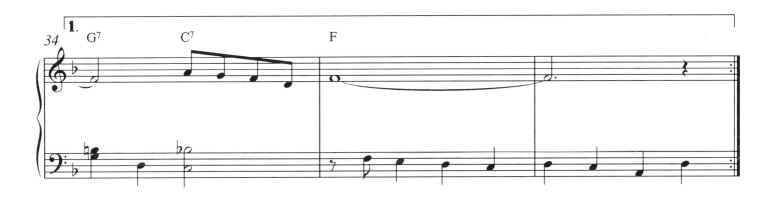

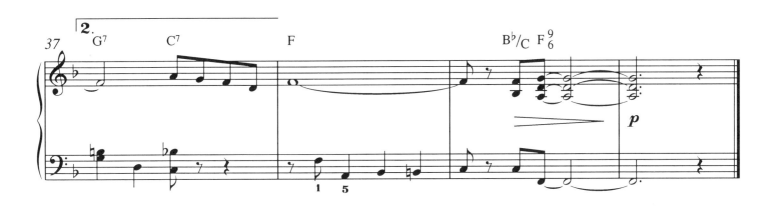

I'll Remember April

Words & Music by Don Raye. Gene de Paul & Patricia Johnson

Moderately bright

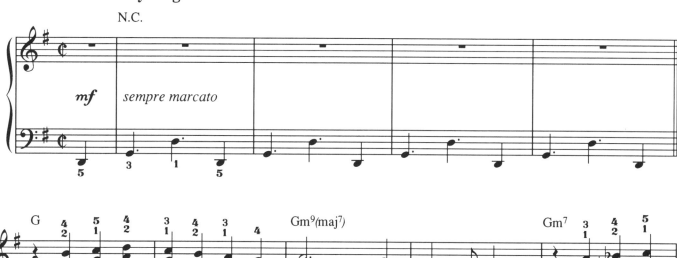

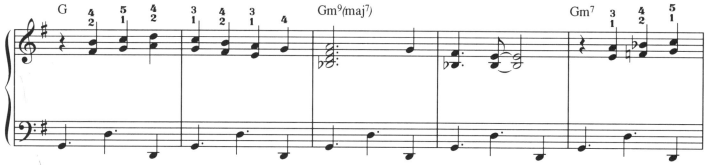

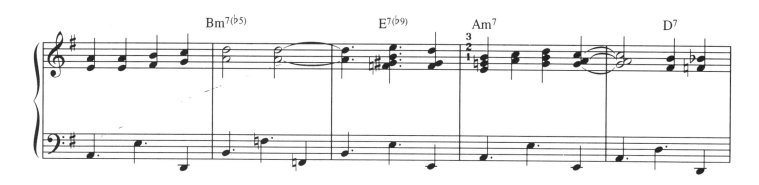

I'm Beginning To See The Light

Words & Music by Harry James, Duke Ellington, Johnny Hodges & Don George

In A Sentimental Mood

Words & Music by Duke Ellington, Irving Mills & Manny Kurtz

In The Mood

Words by Andy Razaf. Music by Joe Garland

The Lady Sings The Blues

Words by Billie Holiday. Music by Herbie Nichols

Moderately

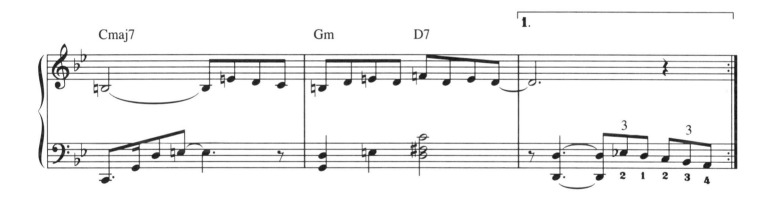

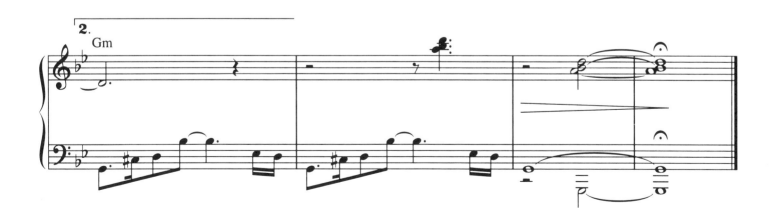

Little Brown Jug

Traditional

Medium swing

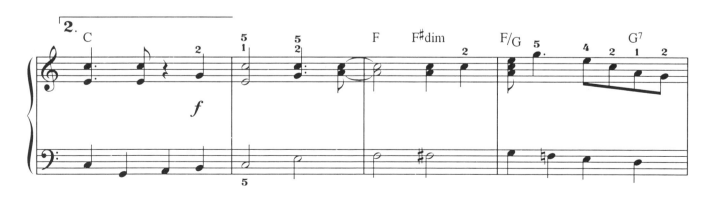

Lover Man (Oh Where Can You Be)

Words & Music by Jimmy Davis, Roger Ram Ramirez & Jimmy Sherman

Lullaby of Birdland

Music by George Shearing. Words by George David Weiss

L'il Darlin'
(Don't Dream Of Anybody But Me)

Words by Bart Howard. Music by Neal Hefti

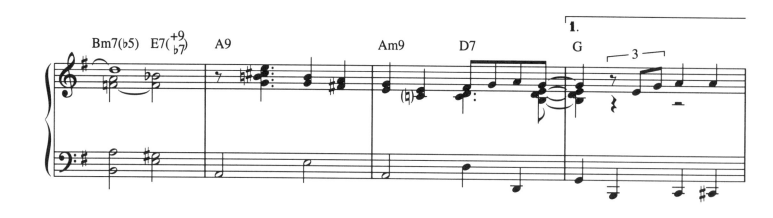

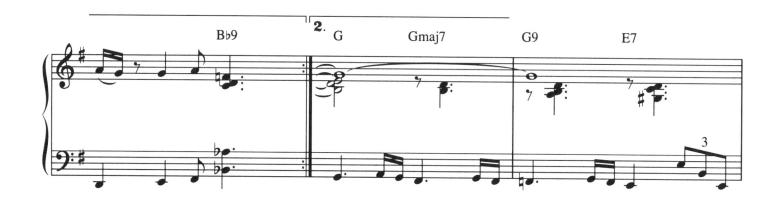

Manhattan Spiritual

By Billy Maxted

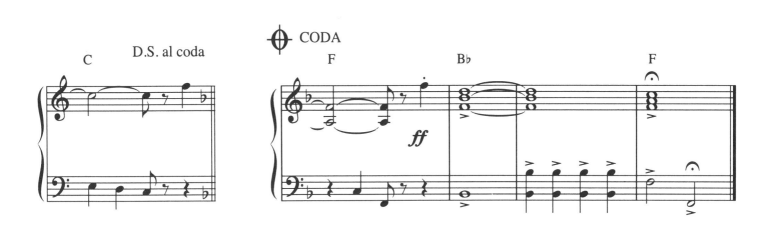

Night Train

Words by Oscar Washington and Lewis C. Simpkins. Music by Jimmy Forrest.

The Old Piano Roll Blues

Words & Music by Cy Coben

One Note Samba
(Samba De Uma Nota So)

Original Words by N. Mendonca English Lyric by Jon Hendricks. Music by Antonio Carlos Jobim

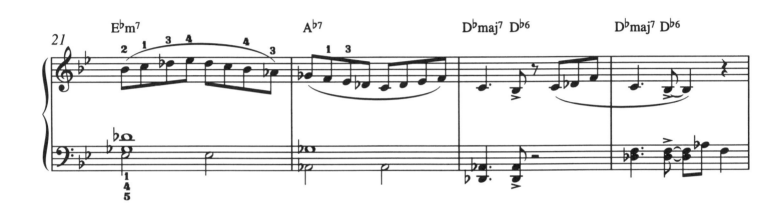

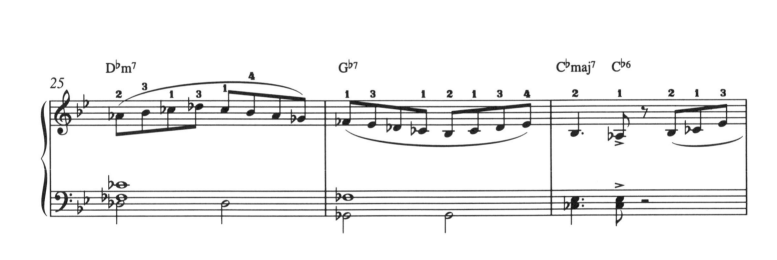

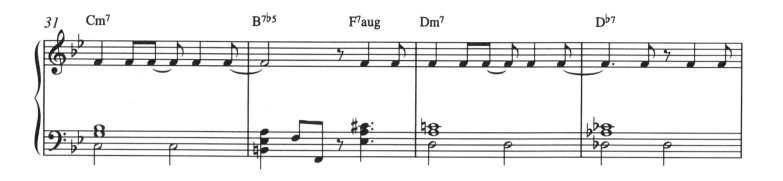

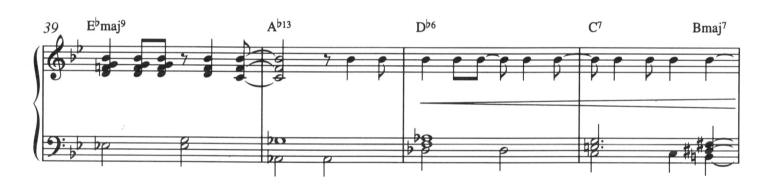

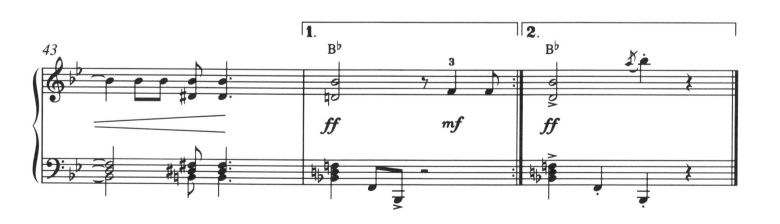

Pennies From Heaven

Words by John Burke. Music by Arthur Johnston

Pick Yourself Up

Music by Jerome Kern. Words by Dorothy Fields

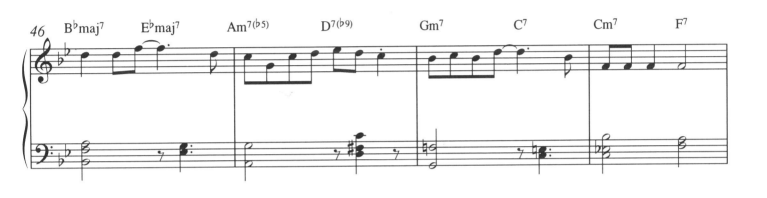

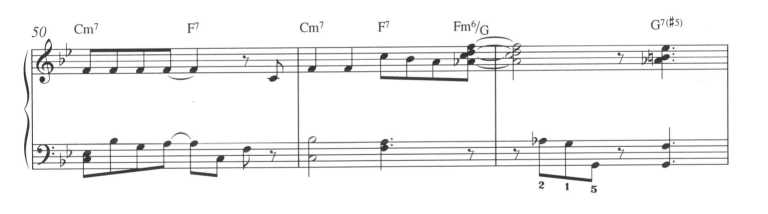

Prelude No. 2

By George Gershwin

Quince

By Sonny Stitt

Moderately slow

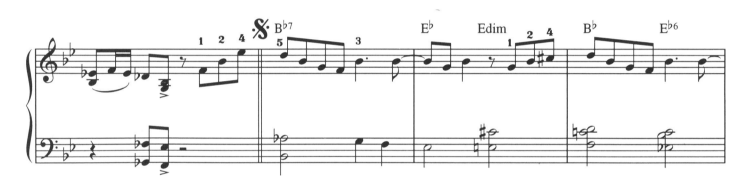

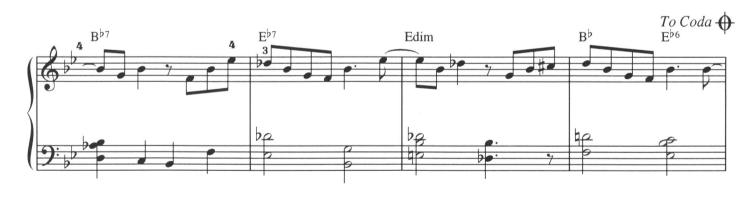

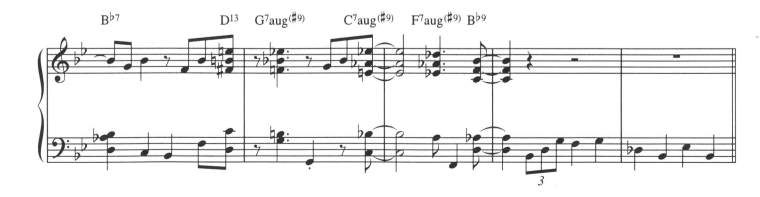

Quiet Nights Of Quiet Stars
(Corcovado)

English Words by Gene Lees. Music & Original Words by Antonio Carlos Jobim

Moderately

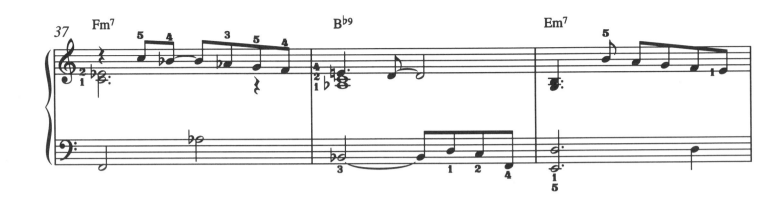

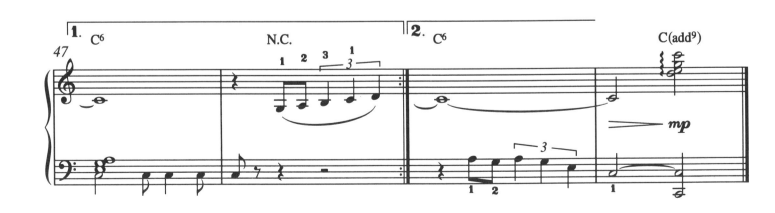

'Round Midnight

By Cootie Williams & Thelonious Monk

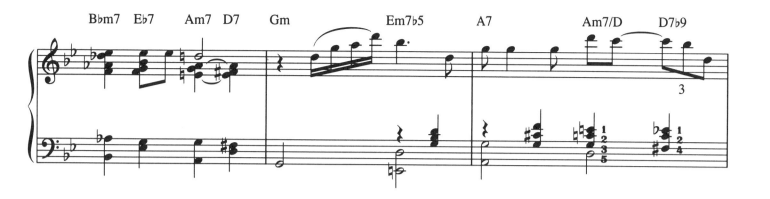

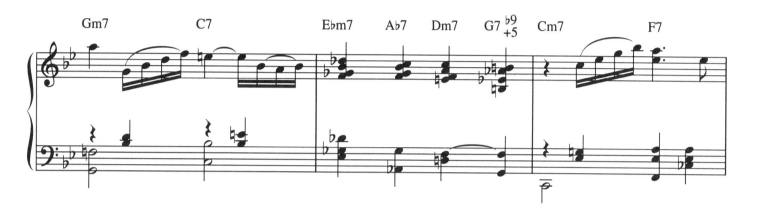

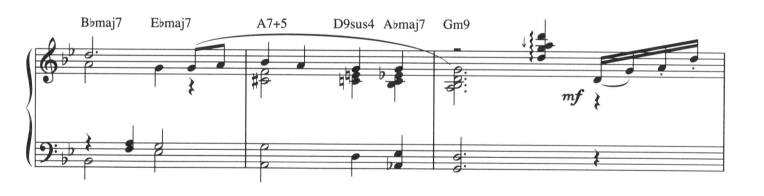

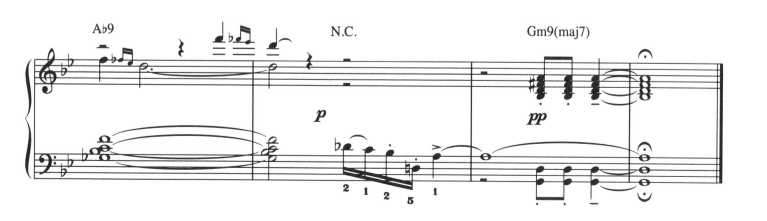

Satin Doll

Words by Johnny Mercer. Music by Duke Ellington & Billy Strayhorn

114

Sophisticated Lady

Words by Irving Mills & Mitchell Parish. Music by Duke Ellington

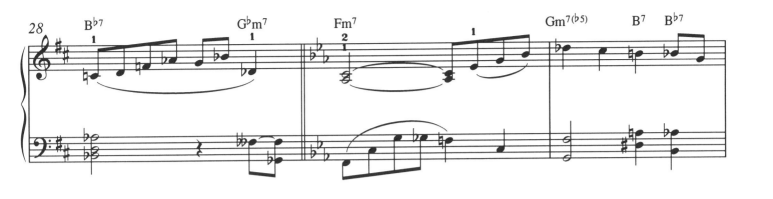

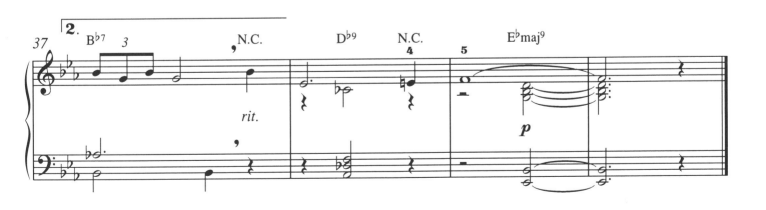

Solitude

Words by Eddie de Lange & Irving Mills. Music by Duke Ellington

Stella By Starlight

Words by Ned Washington. Music by Victor Young

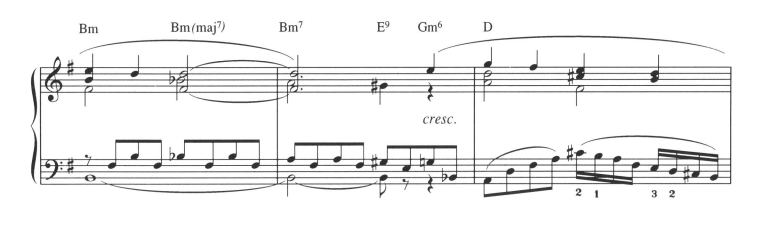

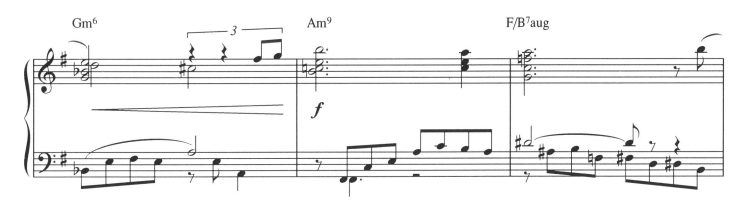

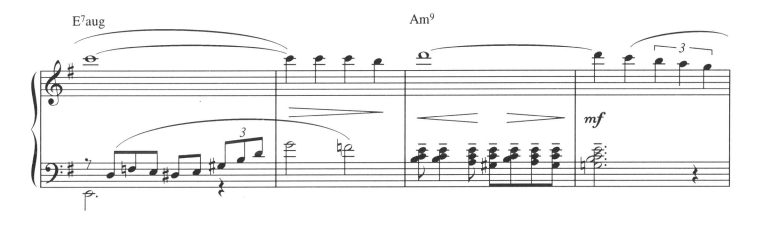

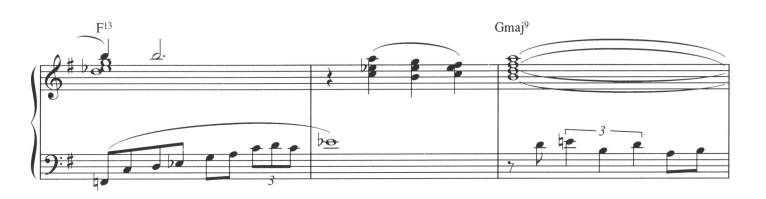

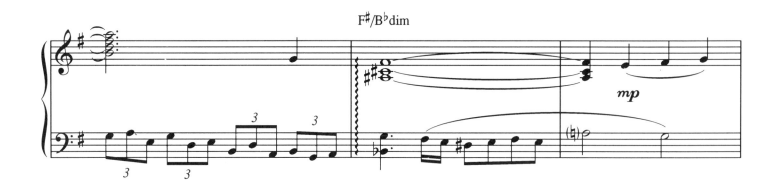

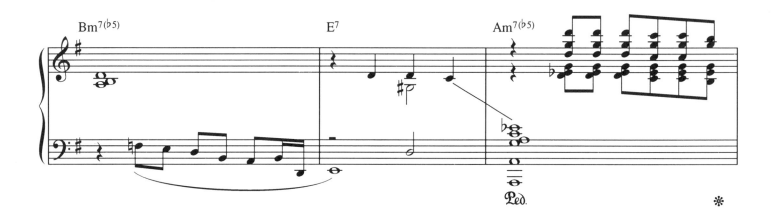

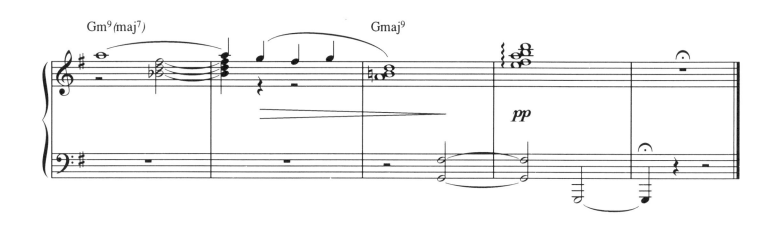

The Girl From Ipanema
(Garota De Ipanema)

Original Words by Vinicius De Moraes. English Lyric by Norman Gimbel. Music by Antonio Carlos Jobim

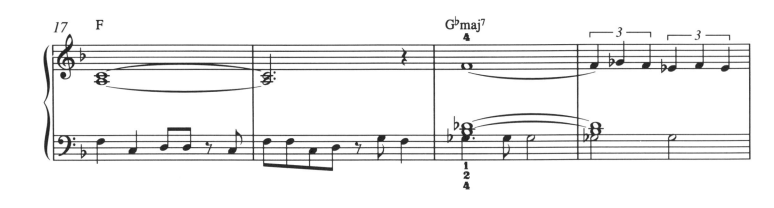

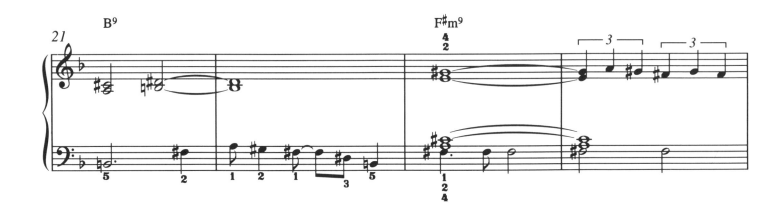

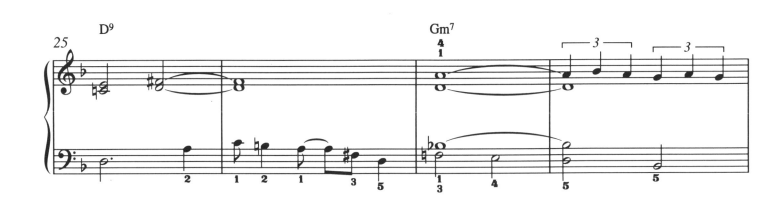

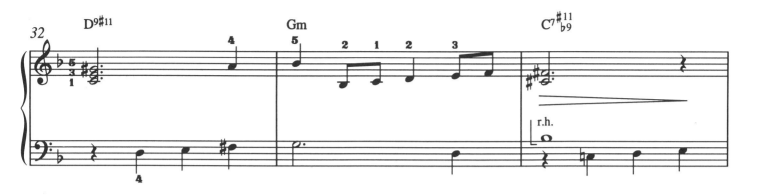

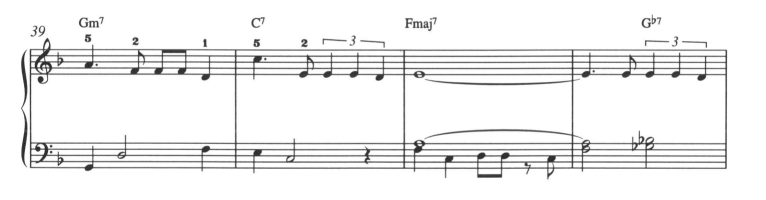

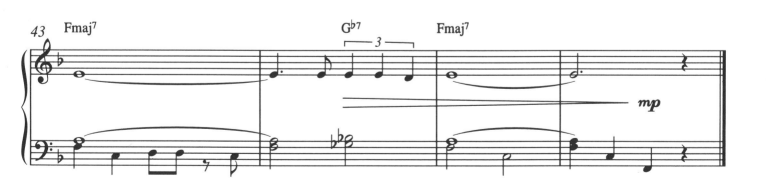

Take The 'A' Train

Words & Music by Billy Strayhorn

That Ole Devil Called Love

Words & Music by Doris Fisher & Allan Roberts

Walking Shoes

By Gerry Mulligan

When Sunny Gets Blue

Words by Jack Segal. Music by Marvin Fisher

You Brought A New Kind Of Love To Me

Words & Music by Sammy Fain, Irving Kahal & Pierre Norman Connor

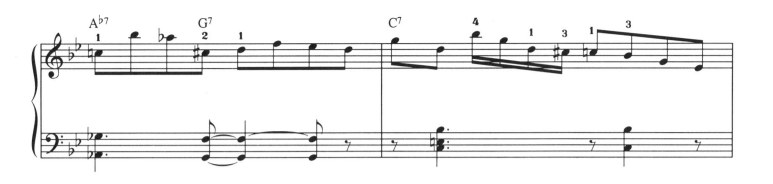

D.S. al Coda

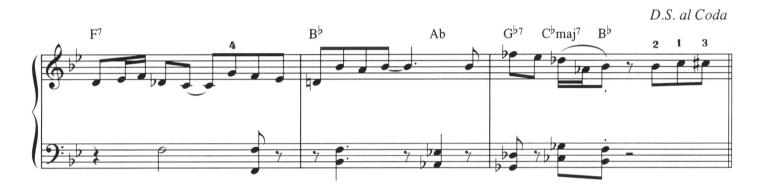

CODA

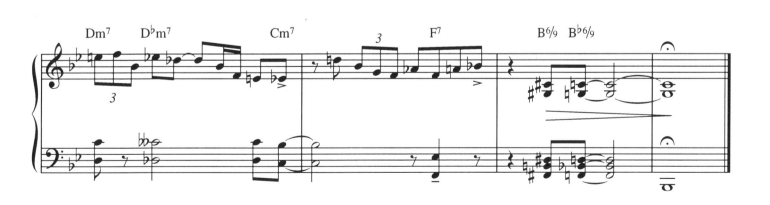

The Night We Called It A Day

Words by Tom Adair. Music by Matt Dennis

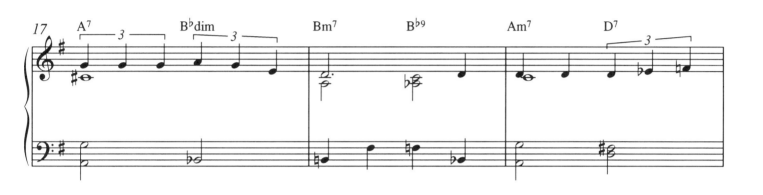

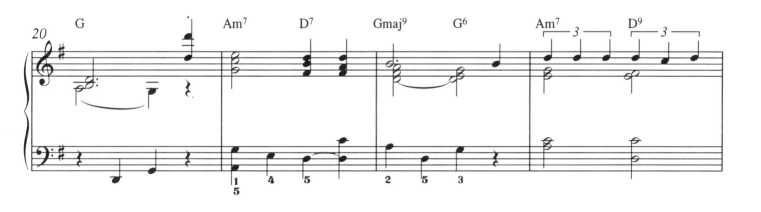

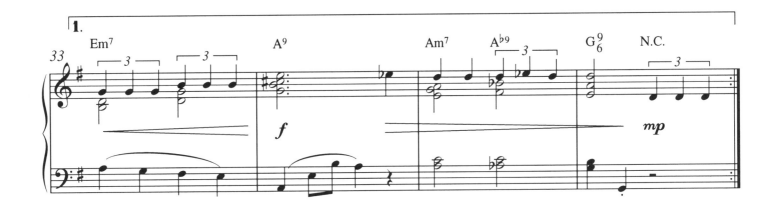

7/01 (40819)